Nick Newman was born in 1958,
and began contributing regularly to
Private Eye in 1981 — including strips
such as Bood, Forbidden Alliance,
Poattle for Britain, Snipcock & Tweed
and Dan Dire. He has written for
Spitting Image, and draws for a
number of publications, including
The Sunday Times, The Guardian,
The Spectator and The Independent
Magazine. In his spare time he works.

THE BEST OF
Newman

MASONS' CHRISTMAS PARTY

PRIVATE EYE · CORGI

"Withhold the front page!"

To Phoebe and Silas

These jokes originally appeared in PRIVATE EYE
Published in Great Britain
by Private Eye Productions Ltd,
6 Carlisle Street, London W1V 5RG,
in association with Corgi Books

© 1990 Pressdram Ltd
ISBN 0 552 13753 7
Designed by Bridget Tisdall
Printed in Great Britain by
The Bath Press, Bath, Avon

Corgi Books are published by Transworld Publishers Ltd,
61-63 Uxbridge Road, Ealing, London W5 5SA,
in Australia by Transworld Publishers (Australia) Pty, Ltd,
15-23 Helles Avenue, Moorebank, NSW 2170
and in New Zealand by Transworld Publishers (N.Z.) Ltd,
Cnr. Moselle and Waipareira Avenues, Henderson, Auckland

"I came here to see Mr Punch —
not Mr Punch's understudy!"

"Let me just look at your notes. . ."

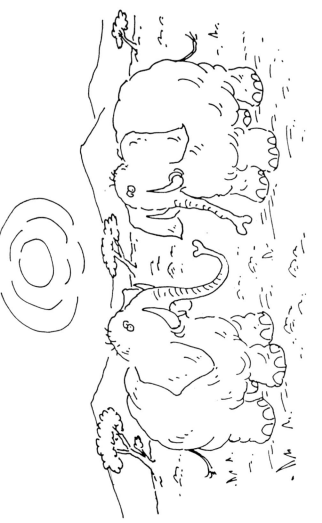

"What is it we're never supposed to do?"

"Oh no! Synchronised Ladies of the Lake!"

"He's doing the knowledge"

"Hello — Dyslexics Amonynous?"

GATWICK
ALL FLIGHTS
DELAYED

"On the bright side, by the time we get there they may have
finished the hotel"

①

②

"You're ruthless, Collins. I like that in a manager"

"This hypochondria — can you give me something for it?"

"Good afternoon — we're recruitment consultants for His Majesty's Navy"

"Come back! I was just getting ready!"

"I hope this doesn't mean flares are coming back"

"Sorry, didn't we tell you? We changed it to best out of three. . ."

"Bloody pea-green boat people!"

"All these exposés could make us look very silly indeed"

"I'd like you to meet the rest of the family"

"He's a belly-in-the door journalist . . .

"We'll have you on your feet in no time, Mr Perkins"

"Hold the third page"

"It's all changed since Dr Frankenstein went private"

"Do I hear £100 million?"

"Now, Mother Hubbard,
exactly how bare is
this cupboard?"

"God warned me that it was Wimbledon fortnight"

"Not another bloody sequel!"

"Mmm . . . I think I'll have that one . . ."

"I'm afraid there's a waiting list for heart operations"

"It's a digital
dandelion"

"Don't worry Mrs Dumpty — we're doing everything
we can to talk your son out of it. . ."

①

②

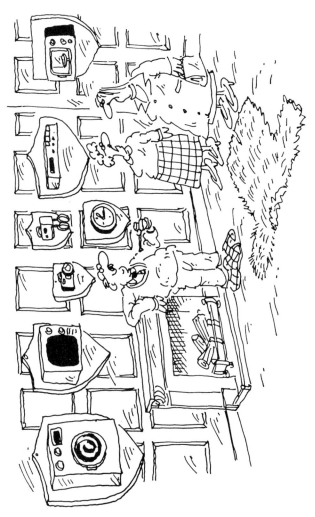

"Gerald fancies himself as a bargain hunter"

"It fell off the back of a lorry. . ."

"We do concerts, parties — and contract demolition work"

"I'm off to do my Christmas shoplifting. . ."

"He's changed his mind. He wants to be cremated"

"You're run-down, Mr Perkins — but you've come to the right place"

". . . a threat to society and a danger to women — but enough about me. . ."

"It's how the old scoutmaster wanted it. . ."

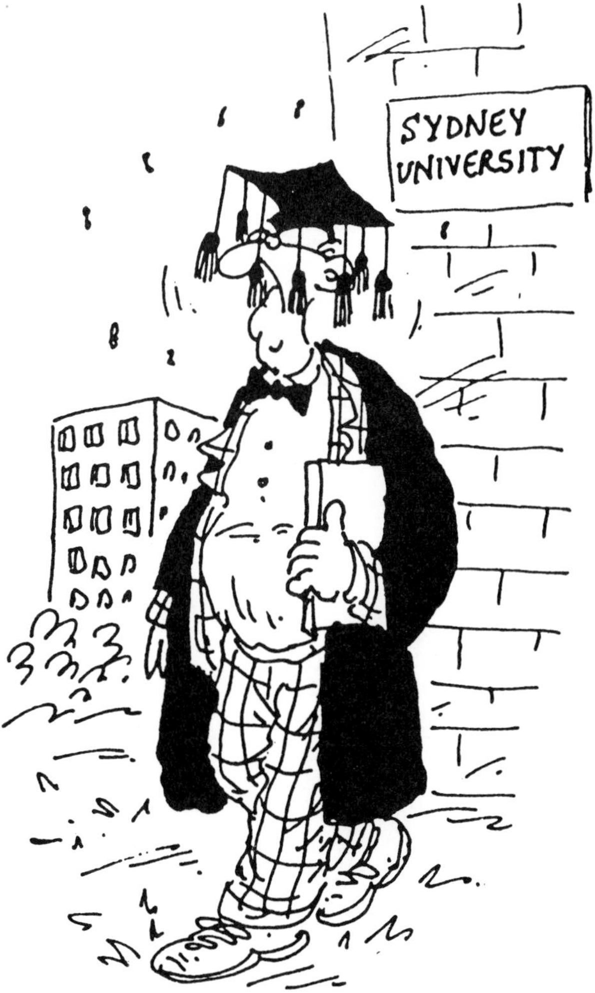
SYDNEY
UNIVERSITY

"I'm afraid you've got footrot"

"When mortgage rates went up
I had to sell the shoe"

"Your Palace
or mine?"

"Son, it's a jungle out there"

"Isn't it funny how you still feel hungry after you've eaten a Chinese restaurant..."

"It's from Godot — he's got a job as a bus driver"

"I've just seen the first retired colonel of spring"

"It must be Frank Bough's
old dressing room"

"It's just a crying shame the rest of the band was unavailable"

"Mind if we join you?"

"It was Stig's last wish"

"Poor chap thinks he's suffering from delusions. . ."

"Not for me, thank you — it keeps me awake all afternoon"

"He's a disgrace to lemmings!"

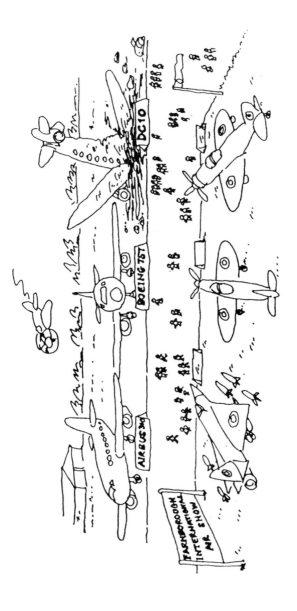

"Bloody hippy convoys!"

"This is our first attempt at home decorating!"

"This saves a lot of time on Christmas day. It's already broken"

"Aye, hovermowers have a lot to answer for"

"I think I preferred the 10 green bottles"

"This AIDS business
is getting out of hand"

"Well, it's a relief to know the poltergeist has a
sense of humour. . ."

"I'm an encyclopaedia salesman. . ."

"You'll be relieved to know he was wearing clean underpants"

"Aye, Jim lad, it's the last time I face a West Indies pace attack"

"We're not going to take this sitting down"

"It's the Bishop of Durham's"

"It's always dangerous putting a prick under a balloon"

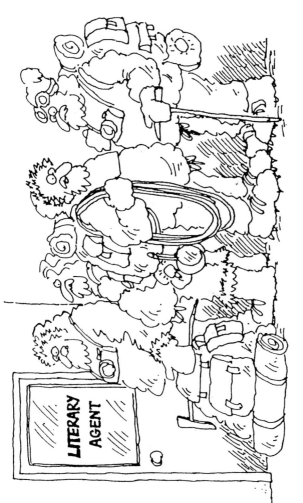

"I remember when we used to do it because it was there..."

"Oh no! The Cow's burning up on re-entry!"

"We don't all go around with black capes and scythes, you know. . ."

"I can never resist a conga!"

"It may be the Solstice — but it's also Ascot week."

"I can't afford the dough"

"Waiter..."

①

②

"Typical — you wait ages for a horseman of the apocalypse —
and then four come along"

"We're occupying the moral high ground. Then we're selling it off to developers"

"Hello - I'm a Jehovah's opinion pollster"

"I'm afraid I've sold the exclusive story to the Bible"

"The job market's collapsed.
Now we're only accepting
people with two old
school ties. . ."

"It's serious. He thinks he's Michael Jackson"

"It's remarkable what modern surgery can do!"

"The invitation most definitely says it's a cheese and wino party"

*"Suspects proceeding towards
Never-Never Land. . ."*

"The moon's always been a bit of a bugger"